Time-Sav
for Teachers

WRITING FICTION YEARS 3-4

W
FRANKLIN WATTS
LONDON • SYDNEY

How to use this book

This book provides a range of worksheets suitable for children in Years 3 and 4 of primary school. The worksheets are grouped into sections which correspond to the text types specified in the National Literacy Strategy. The contents are equally relevant to the Scottish 5-14 Guidelines, and the curricula for the Republic and Northern Ireland.

Each section starts with an introduction. As well as introducing the worksheets, this also details the National Literacy Strategy objectives and suggests approaches to writing. The worksheets have been carefully selected to cater for *different* levels of ability.

At the end of the section, text frames and scaffolds provide guidance for *creative writing* assignments. There are also *assessment sheets* to enable you to keep track of individual children's progress. All teacher-pages have a vertical stripe down the side of the page.

All the worksheets in this book are photocopiable.

This edition first published in 2004

Franklin Watts
338 Euston Road, London NW1 3BH

Contributors: John Barwick, Sharon Dalgleish, Tanya Dalgleish, Karen Dobbie, Ann Doherty, Michael Faye, Angela Lloyd, Sharon Shapiro
UK adaptation by Brenda Stones
Educational advisers: Sarah St John, Jo Owston

This edition not for sale outside the United Kingdom and Eire

ISBN 978 0 7496 5805 2

Printed in Dubai

Franklin Watts is a division of Hachette Children's Books.

Contents

NLS Framework

Year 3

	TERM 1	TERM 2	TERM 3
Fiction and poetry	• stories with familiar settings • plays • poems based on observation and the senses • shape poems	• myths, legends, fables, parables • traditional stories • stories with related themes • oral and performance poetry from different cultures	• adventure and mystery stories • stories by the same author • humorous poetry, poetry that plays with language, word puzzles, puns, riddles

Year 4

	TERM 1	TERM 2	TERM 3
Fiction and poetry	• historical stories and short novels • playscripts • poems based on common themes, e.g. space, school, animals, families, feelings, viewpoints	• stories/novels about imagined worlds: sci-fi, fantasy adventures • stories in series • classic and modern poetry, including poems from different cultures and times	• stories/short novels, etc. that raise issues, e.g. bullying, bereavement, injustice • stories by same author • stories from other cultures • range of poetry in different forms, e.g. haiku, cinquain, couplets, lists, thin poems, alphabets, conversations, monologues, syllabics, prayers, epitaphs, songs, rhyming forms and free verse

Text type grid

Genre	Text	Text type	Year / Term
Poetry	Houses	Poem based on observation and the senses	Y3T1
	Honey Sandwich	Shape poem	Y3T1
	The Barbecue	Oral and performance poem	Y3T2
	Rhyme time	Humorous poetry	Y3T3
	Anyone seen my…?	Poem based on common theme	Y4T1
Drama	The Lion and the Mouse	Playscript	Y4T1
	The Little Old Lady Who Lived in a Vinegar Bottle	Playscript	Y4T1
Stories	Callie's Castle	Story with familiar setting	Y3T1
	The Roughtail Lizard Dreaming	Legend	Y3T2
	Two fables	Fables	Y3T2
	The Boy Who Bounced	Fantasy adventure	Y4T2
	Jason's Walk	Story that raises issues	Y4T3

Introduction to Houses

Level: Year 3 Term 1

Text type: Poem based on observation and the senses

NLS objectives:

Y3T1 T6: to read aloud and recite poems, comparing different views of the same subject; to discuss choice of words and phrases that describe and create impact, e.g. powerful and expressive verbs;

Y3T1 T8: to express their views about a story or poem, identifying specific words and phrases to support their viewpoint;

Y3T1 T13: to collect suitable words and phrases in order to write poems and short descriptions.

The text:

Start by reading the poem aloud, with the class having the text in front of them. Things to talk about:

How many verses? What line is repeated as the heading to each verse?

What class of word is the first word after each of these headings?

Can children suggest examples of each kind of house near your school?

How carefully do you think the poet has observed the different kinds of houses?

The worksheets:

The worksheets start with children describing and writing about their own home; then acting out the sense of movement suggested in each verse; and finally picking out the key verbs to discuss and illustrate.

Houses

Some houses
cling with iron claws
to cliff ledges,
where winds crack rocks
splintering into chasms.

Some houses
nestle into slippers
on mossy slopes,
where moonlight weaves
through fine fern fronds.

Some houses
squat on stumpy feet
in grassy paddocks,
where sunlight gleams
on grazing sheep.

Some houses
snuggle into coverlets
beside sandy beaches,
where wild waves wash
sun bleached faces.

Some houses
stand with straight flanks
in inner-city streets,
where children play
on patchwork porches.

Some houses
sprawl over green lawns
along cul-de-sacs,
where children frolic
under splashing hoses.

by Wendy Michaels

Where do you live?

Name ______________________________

'Houses' is a poem that describes six different houses. Think about where you live. Is it a house or a caravan? Talk with a friend about your home, describing some of its features. Now write a poem describing your home on the lines below.

Drama performance

Name ______________________________

Work in a small group. Choose one verse of the poem. Think and talk about how your group could make this verse into a piece of drama. You could also make up some actions to go along with a reading of the verse.

Write your group's ideas on the lines below. Practise your piece, then show it to the rest of the class.

Find the verbs

Name ______________________________

Reread the poem and find the words that the poet has used to make the houses seem as if they are doing something. Write these words on the lines below. These words are called verbs.

____

____

____

Now, in each box, draw something which would normally carry out this action and one that shows the house carrying out this action.

Cling	Nestle	Squat

Snuggle	Stand	Sprawl

Introduction to Honey Sandwich

Level: Year 3 Term 1

Text type: Shape poem

NLS objectives:

Y3T1 T7: to distinguish between rhyming and non-rhyming poetry and comment on the impact of layout;

Y3T1 T14: to invent a range of shape poems, selecting appropriate words and careful presentation. Build up class collections.

The text:

Start by reading the poem aloud, with the class having the text in front of them. Things to talk about:

Does it give a feeling of spreading honey? How does it do that?

Why are the lines written in these shapes? How many different typefaces can children find?

How old do they think the child narrator is?

What is the role of the dog?

Does it rhyme? If not, what makes it a poem?

The worksheets:

The first sheet helps children break down the stages of the poem, to analyse what's happening in it. The second sheet develops the idea of all the senses being affected by the poem, and encourages vocabulary extension. Finally, writing their own concrete shape poems should be an ongoing pleasure throughout Key Stage 2!

Honey Sandwich

I'm hungry. I want a honey sandwich.
Get the bread out and
the great big bread knife...
Nice **big** bit of fresh squashy bread, yum yum yum...
Another **big** bit of fresh squashy bread for the top...
yum yum yum
Now margarine spreading on the breading.
Spread it on with a spreading knife...
Oh! Got some on my arm...lick it off...
Oops! Got some in my hair...
try and get it out with my knife.
Oops! Cut off some hair...
Oops! I spread my head!

Oh! My sandwich lid fell on the floor!

by Elizabeth Honey
From *Honey Sandwich* (Allen & Unwin)

What's happening?

Name ______________________________

Talk about the poem with your friends before you write your answers on the lines below.

Look carefully at the first picture in the poem. What is happening?

____

____

____

What happens to the text after this picture?

____

____

____

Why did the poet create this effect?

____

____

____

Can you find other examples in this poem where the pictures are influencing the shape of the text? Describe them.

____

____

____

____

____

____

Look at the words in the text that are in bold or appear to be handwritten. Why do you think the poet has chosen to write these words in a different script?

____

____

Are your senses affected?

Name ______________________________

Think about your five senses – touch, smell, hearing, seeing and taste.
What effect does the poem have on your senses? Talk about it with a partner.
In the boxes below, write words to describe how your senses were affected.

TASTE

TOUCH

SMELL

HEARING

SEEING

Be a poet!

Name ______________________________

'Honey Sandwich' is a concrete poem. This means that the layout of the words and pictures combine to make a concrete image. Think of some subjects suitable for a concrete poem. Here are some ideas to get you started. How many more can you add?

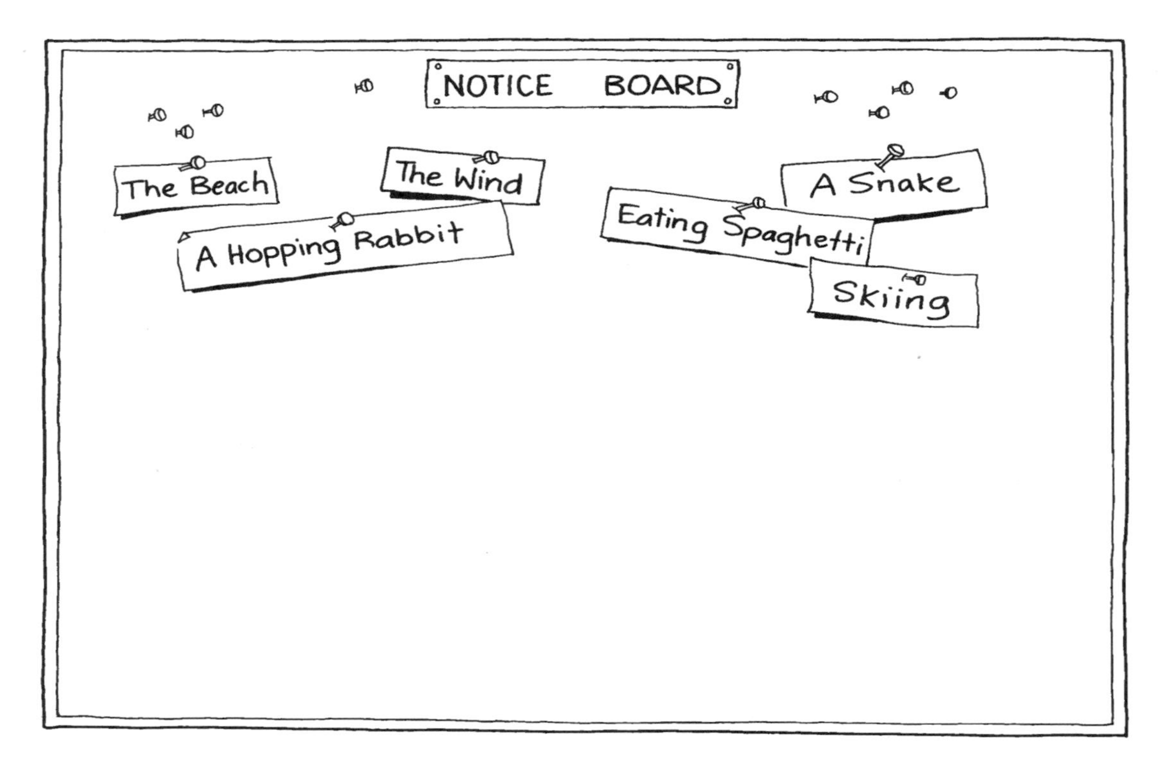

Now choose one idea and write a concrete poem! Write your final version in the space below.

Introduction to The Barbecue

Level: Year 3 Term 2

Text type: Oral and performance poetry

NLS objectives:

Y3T2 T4: to choose and prepare poems for performance, identifying appropriate expression, tone, volume and use of voices and other sounds;

Y3T2 T11: to write new or extended verses for performance based on models of 'performance' and oral poetry read, e.g. rhythms, repetition.

The text:

Choose children to read the poem aloud, taking one verse each.
Things to talk about:

Can children hear the distinct rhythm? How many syllables are there in every line?

Can children hear the pattern of rhymes? Which lines rhyme in every verse? Which lines rhyme in some of the verses?

There is some wonderful vocabulary in the poem: which are the children's favourite words?

Why does the poem need to be read aloud? Can children start to imagine some of the movements they could put to the poem, as a small performance?

The worksheets:

The worksheets help build towards the performance of the poem: first defining the actions in each verse; then thinking about the images in the poem to be portrayed; and finally, planning the physical performance.

The Barbecue

Last Sunday at our barbecue
While blue smoke rose in curls and wisps
My dad played chef in hat and coat
Converting chops to carbon crisps.

Our hungry guests were gathered round
With comments of profundity
About the apron that disguised
His evident rotundity.

The folding table standing near
Was piled with salads, cheese and bread,
With butter, sauce and bottled beer,
So all was ready for the spread.

But Bumblefoot, our dog, of course—
A clumsy, sausage-snatching hound—
Knocked out the trestle table legs
So meat and salads strewed the ground.

Dad blindly grabbed the hot-plate then
To save its equilibrium,
And with a roar of pain and rage
Began to barbecue his thumb.

The outcome, as you well may guess,
Was that we starved and mourned our plight,
While Bumblefoot cleaned up the mess
And burped in ecstasy all night.

by Colin Thiele
From *Poems in My Luggage* (Omnibus/Puffin)

Storyboard the story

Name ____

Read Colin Thiele's barbecue poem. Talk with a friend about the barbecue that the poet describes. Have you ever been at one like this?

In the spaces below make up a storyboard (a cartoon version of the poem) to tell the story. Draw and write the main actions for each verse in the boxes below.

1. ____________________	**2.** ____________________
3. ____________________	**4.** ____________________
5. ____________________	**6.** ____________________

Curls and wisps

Name ______________________________

In this poem there are lots of striking images.
Some of these are identified for you below.
Talk about these images with a partner.

Draw a series of pictures to show how you might portray the images in the poem.

blue smoke rose in curls and wisps	**converting chops to carbon crisps**	**sausage-snatching hound**
meat and salads strewed the ground	**began to barbecue his thumb**	**burped in ecstasy all night**

Share your pictures with your partner. Talk about how you have portrayed these images.

Drama performance!

Name ______________________________

Work with a group of four or five friends to recite the poem. You will need to plan who will say the different lines in the poem, think about how your voices could be used – together or in different combinations, and think about how you could move your bodies to show the movement of the words in the poem.

Use the space below to make notes to help your group plan the activity.

Introduction to Rhyme time

Level: Year 3 Term 3

Text type: Humorous poetry

NLS objectives:

Y3T3 T6: to compare forms or types of humour, e.g. by exploring, collecting and categorising form or type of humour, e.g. word play, joke poems, word games, absurdities, cautionary tales, nonsense verse, calligrams;

Y3T3 T15: to write poetry that uses sound to create effects, e.g. onomatopoeia, alliteration, distinctive rhythms.

The text:

There are four separate poems here, the first a classic humorous poem by Michael Rosen; the next two both nursery rhymes that play with substituted lines, the first rhyming and the second not; and the last is an example of a limerick.

Ask children to read the poems aloud. Things to talk about:

What makes the Michael Rosen poem funny?

Which of the nursery rhymes do children prefer, and why?

Does anyone know other limericks by heart?

The worksheets:

Riddles are a similar form of humour, and children could write or draw ones they know. There are endless possibilities for rewriting well-known nursery rhymes. The work on Michael Rosen's poem should help children analyse exactly what makes it funny, by writing a parody of their own. Finally, there is help on defining the pattern of limericks, and writing their rhyming poetry.

Rhyme time

Down behind the dustbin
I met a dog called Sid.
He could smell a bone inside
but couldn't lift the lid.

by Michael Rosen from
Wouldn't you like to know
(Puffin)

Humpty Dumpty sat on a wall.
Humpty Dumpty had a great fall.
All the King's horses and all the King's men
Had fried eggs and bacon for breakfast again.

from *All Right, Vegemite!* compiled by June Factor (Oxford University Press)

Old Mother Hubbard
Went to the cupboard
To fetch her poor dog a bone.
When she got there
Her cupboard was bare
So the poor little dog had Pal.

from *All Right, Vegemite!* compiled by June Factor (Oxford University Press)

There once was a man from Barcoo
Who discovered a mouse in his stew.
Said the waiter, "Don't shout
And wave it about,
Or the rest will be wanting one too."

(Anonymous)

What a joke!

Name ______________________________

We often have fun with words – making jokes, puns and riddles.
Do you know any riddles? Share these with a friend and write one on the lines below.

____

____

Draw a clue to your riddle here.

New rhymes from old

Name ______________________________

Read the versions of 'Humpty Dumpty' and 'Old Mother Hubbard'. The last line of each of these rhymes has been changed. In 'Humpty Dumpty' the rhyme still works, but in 'Old Mother Hubbard' there is no rhyme. Talk with a small group about what is funny in these nursery rhymes. Write your group's ideas in the space below.

____

____

____

____

____

Choose some nursery rhymes and write your own new versions by changing the last lines. You may wish to keep the same rhyme or change it. Try to make your poem funny. Do your rough work on paper and then write your final version of each rhyme in the space below. You could also draw some pictures to go with your rhymes to make them even funnier!

____

____

____

____

____

____

____

____

____

____

____

____

____

Rhyming lines

Name ______________________________

In the poem by Michael Rosen there are two rhyming lines and two lines which do not rhyme. In the rhyming lines the dog's name forms part of the rhyme. Some of the humour comes from this rhyme.

Below are three names that are sometimes given to dogs. Think of three more names and write them in the spaces in the top row.

Now try to find some words that rhyme with these dogs' names and write them in the spaces beneath each name. Share your rhyming words with a friend.

Tricks	Spot	Mack			

Down behind the dustbin...

Name ______________________________

Using the pattern of the poem, and some of your rhyming words, write more verses to the poem. You may wish to do your rough work on paper and write your finished verses in the space below. Here's one verse to get you started.

Down behind the dustbin
I met a dog called Sam.
He said he wouldn't eat the bone
He'd prefer brown bread and jam.

____
____
____
____

____
____
____
____

____
____
____
____

Take turns to read your poems to the rest of the class. Talk about what makes the rhymes funny. Draw pictures of some of the funny parts next to your poems.

Limericks

Name ______________________________

A limerick is a five line poem which tells a story about a funny or fantastical incident. The first, second and fifth lines are longer and rhyme with each other, while the third and fourth lines are shorter and also rhyme with each other.

Read the limerick 'There once was a man from Barcoo'. Talk with a friend about why this is funny or fantastical. Notice the rhyme scheme and the rhythm.

In this list of sixteen words there are eight pairs of rhyming words.
Find the pairs of words that rhyme and write them on the lines below.

tough	bread	enough	twirl
stood	pearl	hood	die
said	sty	hare	mare
blow	here	dear	flow

____

____

____

____

____

Write words that rhyme next to the words below.

young ____________ crow ____________ lace ____________

showers ____________ town ____________ four ____________

Complete the limerick.

A silly young man named Joe

Moved the hay but was way too slow.

He ______________________________

____

____

There once was a...

Name ______________________________

Write your own limericks. Follow the rhyme pattern and try to capture the rhythm pattern. Work on rough paper and write your final versions in the space below. Here are some ideas to get you started.

There once was a woman from Poole

____
____
____
____

A wonderful bird is the eagle

____
____
____
____

____
____
____
____
____

____
____
____
____
____

____
____
____
____
____

Introduction to Anyone seen my...?

Level: Year 4 Term 1

Text type: Poem based on common theme

NLS objectives:

Y4T1 T7: to compare and contrast poems on similar themes, particularly their form and language, discussing personal responses and preferences;

Y4T1 T14: to write poems based on personal or imagined experience, linked to poems read. List brief phrases and words, experiment by trimming or extending sentences; experiment with powerful and expressive verbs.

The text:

Ask children to read the poem aloud, taking one verse each.
Things to talk about:

Who do children identify with in the poem? Who in the class is always losing things? Who never loses things?

Which line is used to start every verse, except one? Why do children think there's one exception?

Analyse the structure of the poem: How many lines to each verse? How many syllables in each line? Which lines rhyme?

The worksheets:

The first two sheets are on planning a performance of the poem, with actions. The third is for writing, using the pattern of the poem as a model text.

At the end of this section there are further templates to help children plan and write their own poetry.

Anyone seen my...?

The people who keep losing things
Are searching high and low.
They poke and peer – "We left it here."
But no-one seems to know.

The people who keep losing things
Have not a single clue.
They look in vain – "It's lost, *again*.
I can't just wear *one* shoe."

For people who keep losing things
There isn't any cure.
They carry on – "It *can't* be gone.
I left it there, I'm *sure*."

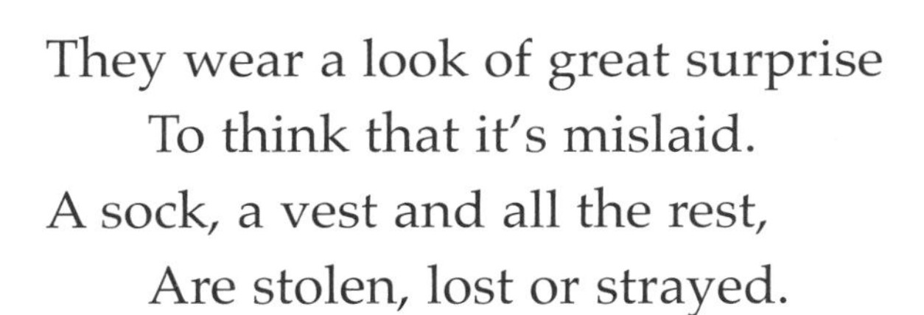

They wear a look of great surprise
To think that it's mislaid.
A sock, a vest and all the rest,
Are stolen, lost or strayed.

The people who keep losing things –
They worry and they whine.
They can't think where ... but, most unfair,
They go and borrow mine.

by Max Fatchen

From *Songs For My Dog and Other People* (Puffin)

Lights! Camera! Action!

Name ______________________________

Imagine that you are a famous film director and create a storyboard for the poem. A storyboard is a cartoon version of the poem. It is used as a shooting script. You will need to think carefully about what you want to include in each frame, and whether you want it to be a long shot, mid-shot or close-up. Under each frame in your cartoon write the dialogue plus notes about any special effects, sound effects or music.

dialogue and notes			
dialogue and notes			

What a performance!

Name ______________________________

Work with a group of friends to prepare a performance of the poem. Choose different group members to speak different lines. Practise using or joining your voices in interesting ways. You might like to try varying the pitch, tone or rhythm. You'll need to rehearse before you perform for the rest of the class!

Design time

Create a poster or cover for a flyer to advertise your group's performance of the poem. Use this space to experiment with different lettering styles before you make your good copy.

Be a poet!

Name ______________________________

Talk with a partner about other things that you could complain about in a poem. How about the people who never do their homework or the people who are always late? What other ideas can you add? Now choose one of the ideas and write your own poem! Use this space to list and draft your ideas.

Things I could write about

____

____

____

____

____

____

____

Draft ideas

____

____

____

____

____

____

____

____

____

____

I HATE PEOPLE WHO COMPLAIN.

Now revise, edit and proofread your poem!

Wish poems

Name ___________________________________

Complete the wish poem. Then draw a picture to add some humour to the poem.

I wish ...

I wish I could climb that gnarled old tree,
I wish it was not so difficult for me.

I wish I could sing all the hits on that chart,
I wish I could hit the bull's eye with my dart.

I wish ___________________________________
I wish ___________________________________

I wish ___________________________________
I wish ___________________________________

I wish ___________________________________
I wish ___________________________________

I wish ___________________________________
I wish ___________________________________

Poems with a twist

Name ______________________________

Write some poems with a twist. These are simple, four-line poems which describe a scene. The three lines follow one another and then a twist appears in the fourth line. Illustrate your poems in the boxes. Here's a poem to get you started.

Colourful umbrellas
Yellow raincoats
Black wellies
No rain.

Ballad scaffold

Name ____________________

A ballad is a poem or a song which tells a story. The verses are short and rhyme. One verse is repeated, like a chorus, and is called a refrain. Here is an example of a refrain. Now use this sheet to write your own ballad!

> Sweet Susie is her name,
> Robbery is her game.
> I was in the town when
> she came out,
> They shut the doors
> when she was about!

Orientation:

____

____

Repeated refrain:

____

____

____

____

Complication:

____

____

____

____

(Repeated refrain)

Series of events:

____

____

____

____

(Repeated refrain)

Resolution:

____

____

____

____

(Repeated refrain)

Poetry writing interview

Name ______________________________

Self-assessment e.g. What type of poetry do you enjoy writing or reading? Is there any poetry that you would like to write that you haven't yet tried? Is there anything you don't like writing about or find difficult about writing poetry? How do you rate yourself as a poet?

Range and preferences e.g. What do you like writing poetry about and for what type of audiences? How do you make your poetry clear and interesting?

Skills e.g. How do you plan your poems? How do you edit your work? Are your ideas more important, or accurate spelling and correct sentence structure? How do you check spelling if you are unsure of a word?

Current projects e.g. What poems are you writing now? What would you like to write?

Poetry writing assessment

Name ______________________________

Task e.g. Rhyming, sensory, humorous, descriptive poetry
Context e.g. Individual, pairs, group, teacher directed

ANALYSIS

Content e.g. Purpose, organisation of verses or format, awareness of audience
Skills e.g. Planning, drafting, editing, redrafting, spelling, punctuation, handwriting
Language study e.g. Selection of appropriate sensory and descriptive language
Teaching needs e.g. Attitude to task, teaching needed for further development

Introduction to Drama

Level: Year 4 Term 1

Text type: Playscripts

NLS objectives:

This is the one point in Years 3–4 that the NLS concentrates on playscripts:

Y4T1 T5: to prepare, read and perform playscripts; compare organisation of scripts with stories – how are settings indicated, story lines made clear?

Y4T1 T6: to chart the build-up of a play scene, e.g. how scenes start, how dialogue is expressed, and how scenes are concluded;

Y4T1 T13: to write playscripts, e.g. using known stories as basis.

The texts:

These are two contrasting playscripts, for reading aloud or working up into a performance. Things to talk about:

First look at the layout on the page. How can you tell who's speaking? How are the stage directions displayed?

Then allocate parts and read around the class.

Analyse the different characters. Is this easier to do with a playscript?

Analyse the development of the plot. How is dialogue used to move the action forward? Discuss the structure of orientation, complication, resolution and epilogue.

Work towards a performance of the play.

Children then try writing their own playscripts, following the model layout of the texts provided.

The worksheets:

The worksheets for both scripts provide support for analysing the elements of the dramas: character, plot, speech patterns and sound effects, and help pupils move towards performance and then writing. The final section gives further templates to help with drama writing.

The Lion and the Mouse (part 1)

Characters:

Mouse 1 (female)

Mouse 2 (male)

Lion (male)

Jungle noises: animals scampering; birds singing; movement of branches.

Mouse 1: Over here.

Mouse 2: Where?

Mouse 1: Come on. This way.

Mouse 2: No – it's too dangerous. There's nowhere to hide.

Mouse 1: Are you a scaredy mouse?

Mouse 2: No – but I don't want to be eaten by a lion.

Mouse 1: You are a scaredy mouse. Look, nothing's happening to me. See. Come on over here.

Mouse 2: No!

Danger music.

Mouse 1: Come on you stupid mouse. You've got to learn to be brave.

Mouse 2: No I ... oh no, oh, look out!

Sound of lion roaring and crashing through jungle.

Lion: Got you, you tasty little morsel.

Mouse 1: Let go of my tail. Put me down. Let me go!

Lion: Ha, ha, ha. You're a brave little thing. I shall not let you go. You will make a nice little appetiser before I find the rest of my dinner.

Mouse 1: Please, lion. Don't eat me. Let me go.

Lion: Why ever should I let you go now that I have caught you?

The Lion and the Mouse (part 2)

Mouse 1: If you do me this favour, one day I may be able to help you.

Lion: Help me! I'll say this for you. You certainly are a brave little mouse. Help me! I doubt it. What could a mouse do that a lion cannot do?

Mouse 1: Well we are much smaller than you and can fit into tiny crevices, and nibble at delicate things like string and straw.

Lion: Hmmm. That is certainly true. Well little mouse. I will let you go, just this once. But you must promise that if I ever need your help you will come immediately.

Mouse 1: Of course. Oh thank you lion. I'm sure you will never regret this kindness.

Lion: Hmm. Kindness, humph. Now be off with you before I change my mind.

Mouse 1: Goodbye lion, 'til we meet again.

Lion: Kindness. Humph.

Sounds of lion roaring in glee and crashing through jungle.
Roaring turns from glee to terror and continues for some moments.

Mouse 1: What a dreadful noise. That lion sounds as though he is in trouble.

Mouse 2: Let's get as far away as we can.

Mouse 1: No, I'm going to investigate.

Mouse 2: You'll be killed.

Mouse 1: I promised lion I would help him if he ever needed me.

Mouse 2: Oh, no, not again.

Scampering sounds with lion whimpering in the background.

Lion: Oh, oh, oh, helppppppppp!

Mouse 1: Shh! Lion. What's the matter?

Lion: Look at me. I'm caught in this net.

Mouse 1: How did you manage that?

Lion: I was just walking along my usual path, when this net fell all around me, and now I'm tied up in knots. Oh, oh, oh what a terrible state for a lion to be in.

The Lion and the Mouse (part 3)

Sounds of thrashing around.

Mouse 1: Now listen here lion. You must keep still. The hunter who set this trap will be back soon and I can't set you free if you are moving all over the place.

Lion: You couldn't set me free anyway. I should never have let you go when I did.

Mouse 1: Now listen here, lion, if that is the way you are going to behave I'll just go away and forget the promise I made you.

Lion: Oh, oh, oh. I'll be quiet and still. But how can you get me out of this terrible net trap?

Mouse 1: I told you that mice can nibble through string and straw and fit into small spaces. Stay very still because that is exactly what I am going to do.

Lion: Where are you, mouse?

Nibbling sounds and scampering sounds.

Mouse 1: Do stop talking, lion, so that I can get on with the job.

More nibbling sounds and scampering sounds.

Lion: Ooh, ooh that tickles.

Mouse 1: Now lift your back paws.

Lion: I can't—oh! They're free.

More nibbling and scampering sounds.

Mouse 1: Now your front paws.

Lion: Oh, you are a wonderful mouse.

More nibbling and scampering accompanied by lion giggling.

Mouse 1: Right, there you are, just stretch right up through that hole and you will be free.

Lion: Mouse, I am so grateful I could eat you up.

Mouse 1: Oh no you don't, lion. I'm out of here.

Lion: Wait for me! Where are you? I can't fit in there. Waaaiiit!

Sounds of lion roaring, chasing through the jungle in pursuit of squeaking mouse.

Adapted for radio by *Wendy Michaels*

Scaredy mouse

Name ______________________________

Did you notice that Mouse 1 called Mouse 2 scaredy mouse? Talk with a partner about why she did this. With your partner, take on the role of the two mice and make up a conversation that could happen between the mice after Mouse 1 has set the lion free. Experiment with different things that they might say to each other. Talk about how each of the mice might be feeling about the near escape that Mouse 1 had.

Write one of your conversations in the space below. Remember to show who is talking.

Character descriptions

Name ____________________

The characters in fables are often animals. In this story there are three animals – a lion and two mice. Each character is different. Talk about them with a partner. Try to find words to describe each character. Write some of the words on the lines below. Draw what you think they look like in the spaces.

Lion

____

____

____

____

Mouse 1

____

____

____

____

Mouse 2

____

____

____

____

Sound effects

Name ______________________________

The Lion and the Mouse is a script for a radio play. It sometimes uses sound effects instead of words to tell the audience what is happening. Work with a group of three. Look closely at the sound effect instructions. Talk about what information the audience is being given in each case. Experiment with ways of making these sound effects.

In the space below, create a list of the sound effects and how you will make each of them.

____

____

____

____

____

____

____

____

Work in a group to rehearse the radio play. You will need to choose three people to play the roles of the characters and others to make the sound effects. Make sure that you find the right voices for the characters and have all the sound effects ready.

Perform your version of the play to other groups in the class. You could even record it on tape. Talk in your group about your performance and production of the play. Write your feelings about the performance in the space below.

____

____

____

____

____

____

____

____

____

Advert

Name ______________________________

Talk in a small group about what features of the play you would want to highlight in an advert. List them below, then make up a fifteen-second advert for your play. You may wish to use the voices of the characters as well as a voice to present the advert. Remember that your advert needs to tell the audience when they will be able to hear the play. Work on rough paper and then write your finished advert in the space below. You might even record it on tape.

Features to be highlighted

____

____

____

____

____

Published advert

____

____

____

____

____

____

____

____

____

____

____

____

____

____

____

The Little Old Lady Who Lived in a Vinegar Bottle (part 1)

CHARACTERS:

Narrator	Chickens (4 or 5)
Little Old Lady	Footman
Chorus	Plumed Horses (4)
Kind Fairy	Servants
Maidservant	Townspeople (carrying baskets of wares to sell at the market)

This play is adapted from an old but little-known folktale.

Scenery and costume suggestions:

Costumes should be the traditional fairy story type. The Horses could be all dressed in brown, white or black tights and jumpers. They should have large, colourful plumes on their heads. The Chickens could have similar costumes in yellow, perhaps with orange legs.

The different homes of the Little Old Lady would most easily be shown by large pictures made by the children, as has been suggested in the play. The vinegar bottle could be a frame that the Little Old Lady could sit in.

NARRATOR:
Once upon a time, a long time ago, there was a Little Old Lady who lived in a vinegar bottle. Now she was not very happy living in that vinegar bottle...

LITTLE OLD LADY:
[stepping out of the vinegar bottle]
Well, I ask you – would you be happy, living cramped up in a little bottle? I have no room to move, no room to cook, no room to do anything. It just isn't fair!

CHORUS:
Poor old lady, it isn't fair.
No room to cook or sit on a chair.

NARRATOR:
Well as it happens, one day a fairy was passing by on her travels. She was a kind fairy, and she felt sorry for the Little Old Lady.

LITTLE OLD LADY:
[grumbling away; Fairy listens unseen by her]

The Little Old Lady Who Lived in a Vinegar Bottle (part 2)

'Tis a shame so it is, 'tis a shame that I should have to suffer so.

CHORUS:
'Tis a shame that she should suffer so,
Fairy, can't you make her go?

KIND FAIRY:
Sh!

LITTLE OLD LADY:
I should like to live in a little cottage in the country. I would like to have a maidservant to bring me a cup of tea. I would like a little garden with chickens pecking in the dirt and laying fresh eggs for me. Oh, it just isn't fair that I have to live in this vinegar bottle.

KIND FAIRY:
I think I can help you, Little Old Lady. Tonight, when you go to bed, turn around three times, and in the morning you'll see what you'll see.

[Old lady turns, and slips behind the closing curtain.]

CHORUS:
So she turned around three full times
And, much to her surprise,
In the morning when she awoke
What a sight befell her eyes.

NARRATOR:
Yes, the Little Old Lady was no longer in the vinegar bottle.
[Curtain opens. Two children hold a large picture of a country cottage with flowers, etc. They move aside to reveal the Little Old Lady sitting in a rocking chair. Enter Maidservant carrying a tray with a teapot and a cup and saucer.]

MAIDSERVANT:
Good morning, Ma'am. Here is your cup of tea and some freshly baked scones.

LITTLE OLD LADY:
Aah!
[She smiles, then looks around expectantly. Chickens enter squawking and pecking; they can dance or mime. Maidservant flaps her apron at them, and shoos them off stage. She picks up an egg and brings it to the Little Old Lady.]

LITTLE OLD LADY:
Aah! How happy I am.

The Little Old Lady Who Lived in a Vinegar Bottle (part 3)

NARRATOR:
The Little Old Lady was so happy, but she never thought to say thank you to the Kind Fairy.

CHORUS:
The fairy journeyed North and South,
East, West, and over the sea.
But she often thought of the little old dame
And of how happy she must be.

NARRATOR:
Well, by and by the Kind Fairy returned to visit the Little Old Lady to see how she was enjoying her country cottage. But do you know, that Little Old Lady was grumbling again.

[Little Old Lady enters, and walks in front of the curtain.]

LITTLE OLD LADY:
'Tis a shame so it is, 'tis a shame. Why should I live in this boring house in the country with no one to keep me company but one maidservant and some smelly chickens? Other folk live in grand mansions in town. They can look out of the windows and see the people going to the market. They have horses and a carriage to go driving in, and they have menservants as well as maidservants. Oh, I am so bored! 'Tis a shame, so it is, 'tis a shame that I should suffer so.

CHORUS:
'Tis a shame that she should suffer so.
Fairy, can't you make her go?

NARRATOR:
Well, the Kind Fairy was disappointed, but she was a kind fairy, so she said ...

KIND FAIRY:
I think I can help you, Little Old Lady. Tonight, when you go to bed, turn round three times, and in the morning you'll see what you'll see!

CHORUS:
So she turned three full times
And, much to her surprise,
In the morning when she awoke
What a sight befell her eyes.

[Curtain closes as the Little Old Lady turns.]

by Sue Scott

From *Playabout* (Dellasta)

Let's talk about it!

Name ______________________________

Work in a group of six or seven. In your group, read the script aloud a few times, experimenting with pitch (how high or low your voice is), intonation (how your voice rises and falls), rhythm and emphasis at different times during the dialogue.

What effect do different speech patterns have on the characters and on the story? On the lines below, write some of the ideas you tried and the effect they had.

Speech patterns	Effect

The narrative elements

Name ____

The dialogue, or the words spoken by the characters in the playscript, tells a story in much the same way as a narrative does. In this playscript, what is:

The orientation (setting the scene) ____

____

____

The complication (or problem) ____

____

____

1st event ____

____

____

2nd event ____

____

____

Because this is only an extract, or part, of the play, some of the steps in the narrative are missing. What are they?

____

____

____

____

____

____

CAN YOU DO THESE ?

Hot seat

Name ____

Imagine that you are a reporter. You want to know why the Kind Fairy and the Little Old Lady acted as they did. What questions might you ask them? Plan your questions in the space below.

Questions for the Kind Fairy

____

____

____

____

____

____

____

____

____

____

Questions for the Little Old Lady

____

____

____

____

____

____

____

____

Work in a group of four. One of your group members is to take on the role of the Kind Fairy. The rest of the group members are reporters. The Kind Fairy is in the hot seat and must answer the reporters' questions! When the Kind Fairy has answered all the questions, choose someone to be the Little Old Lady and put them in the hot seat!

You finish it

Name ______________________________

This play needs finishing! Work in a group of six or seven to:

PLAN additional events, find a resolution to the problem and make a final comment.

DRAFT a rough version of your play on scrap paper, remembering this play's special features such as the poetry, recurring patterns in the text and instructions to the actors.

REVISE, EDIT and PROOFREAD your rough draft.

WRITE your final copy, properly formatted as a playscript, below.

Our Play

Drama outline

Name ______________________

Scenery	Main characters

Costumes

Prologue

Orientation

Complication

Series of events

Resolution

Epilogue (optional)

Drama scaffold

Name ______________________________

Characters

____

____

Scenery and costume suggestions

____

____

Prologue

(This is an optional way of introducing the setting and the characters and giving some background information that is important for the play.)

____

____

Orientation

(This is generally shorter than in a narrative.)

Who? ______________________________

____

When? ______________________________

____

Where? ______________________________

____

What situation? ______________________________

____

Why? ______________________________

____

Complication

(A problem occurs in the character's personal life or in the world around him.)

____

____

Series of events

____

____

Resolution

(The problem in the complication is resolved by one of the main characters.)

____

____

Epilogue

____

____

Drama writing interview

Name ______________________________

Self-assessment e.g. What ideas do you enjoy writing about in your playscripts? Is there anything you don't like writing about or find difficult? How do you rate yourself as a scriptwriter?

Range and preferences e.g. What do you like writing about and for what type of audiences? How do you make your dialogue and action clear and interesting? Do you enjoy mime, improvisation or working from a script? Do you think back over your work to see how you could improve it?

Skills e.g. How do you plan your stories? How do you edit your work? How do you create interesting and realistic characters? Do you prefer to develop your characters on your own or with help from your teacher and friends? Are your ideas more important, or accurate spelling and correct sentence structure? How do you check spelling if you are unsure of a word?

Current projects e.g. What dramatic scripts are you writing now? Which parts are you happy with and which do you think need more thought? What would you like to write?

Drama skills checklist

Name:				
Class:	**Date/Level**	**Date/Level**	**Date/Level**	**Date/Level**
PURPOSE				
Demonstrates understanding of the purpose of dramatic scripts.				
STRUCTURE				
Writes a prologue where the scene and background are described.				
Lists characters and costumes, and describes scenery effectively (not for radio scripts).				
Writes a clear but shortened orientation.				
Creates a complication based on an unexpected event.				
Writes a well-developed series of events.				
Able to resolve the situation clearly.				
Able to recognise different types of dramatic scripts.				
TEXT ORGANISATION				
Develops a well-sequenced plan for scriptwriting.				
Able to write a clear sequence of events.				
Writes a resolution connected to the orientation and complication.				
Writes a prologue effectively tying up any incomplete threads.				
LANGUAGE FEATURES				
Makes use of action to develop the events.				
Uses action verbs effectively.				
Consistently uses correct tense.				
Uses dialogue to build up interesting scripts.				
Uses first or third person consistently.				

LEVEL CODES 1 Consistently evident 2 Sometimes evident 3 Not evident

Drama assessment

Name ______________________________

FEATURES	DATE	COMMENTS
Is the pace of the play varied and does the student use pause effectively to build up tension?		
Are the emotions of the play conveyed by the pitch of the voice? How does the pitch of the voice and the intonation suit different characters?		
Does the use of movements, facial expressions and eye contact enhance the play?		
Is sufficient attention paid to how the play begins and how it ends?		
Does an expressive voice effectively convey the mood of the play? Can we hear the anger, happiness, moodiness etc. that the character is feeling?		
Is the storyline conveyed in a sequenced, effective and easy to follow manner?		
Is the student able to take on the role of the character and maintain this in a believable way?		
Is the student confident and able to gain the attention of the audience?		

FOLLOW-UP SUGGESTIONS

Introduction to Callie's Castle

Level: Year 3 Term 1

Text type: Story with familiar setting

NLS objectives:

Y3T1 T3: to be aware of the different voices in stories using dramatised readings, showing differences between the narrator and different characters used, e.g. puppets to present stories;

Y3T1 T12: to investigate and collect sentences/phrases for story openings and endings – use some of these formal elements in re-telling and story writing.

The text:

Read the text aloud to the class. Things to talk about:

What tells us this is probably the opening of the story?
(Note the switch from 1st to 3rd person narration.)

Describe the friendship between Frances and Callie.

What do you think might happen about the letter?

The worksheets:

The first two sheets encourage spoken responses to the story, to embed children's understanding of the narrative. The third sheet suggests a prediction exercise on taking the plot forward, and then a rehearsal for acting out the new plot through a number of narrators.

The final sheet proposes writing a new story on the subject of argument between friends.

Callie's Castle

As I came out of the school gate, I almost turned left along the way I used to walk to my old home. But when I heard Frances calling me, I ran off quickly in the right direction.

Until a week ago, Frances and I had been best friends. What had we quarrelled about? It had been something so small, so silly, that I couldn't remember it. I didn't want to, either, for the fight had ended with me blurting out such cruel things that now my face scorched at the thought of them.

To say such things to Frances! Callie nearly groaned aloud. And yet, as Frances came pounding along behind her, she turned in silence, putting on a hostile face.

"Oh, it's all right!" bristled Frances. "I don't want to talk to you. Mrs Wheeler said you were to give this to your mother."

Callie looked at the envelope, on which was written 'Mrs Beck by courtesy of Callie'.

"Take it yourself!" she said.

Frances glowered. "No I won't, you pig." She threw the letter on the ground and walked away.

Callie waited until Frances had disappeared around the corner. Then she picked up the letter and dawdled down the hill. She was worried. What was Mrs Wheeler writing to her mother about?

On the way home Callie had a daydream about pushing that letter down a drain and saying nothing about it. But Mrs Wheeler would be sure to ask about it. All right then, stand up and say boldly, "My mother says you're a nutty old lady. Teachers ought to stick to teaching and not write letters home about their pupils, my mother says."

Callie could just see Mrs Wheeler's face going red as everyone roared. That would fix her.

by Ruth Park
From *Callie's Castle* (Angus & Robertson)

Let's talk about it!

Name ____________________

This passage is the beginning of the book *Callie's Castle*. Talk with your partner about the events in the passage, and the way Ruth Park has written about them.

Write the main points of your discussion.

How does Callie feel?

Have you ever felt like that? Explain.

Do you think the events could have really happened?

Is the story realistic or fantasy?

Frances and Callie were best friends. What do you value in a friend?

Tell me again

Name ______________________________

Now retell the passage to your partner. Include all the events that you think are important. Listen to your partner's re-telling. Then write answers to the questions below.

In what ways were your re-tellings the same?

____

____

____

____

In what ways were your re-tellings different?

____

____

____

____

Why weren't your re-tellings exactly the same?

____

____

____

____

What do you think may have happened before the beginning of the extract you have read?

____

____

____

____

Prediction

Name ______________________________

What do you think will happen next? Work in a group to make up outlines for three possible storylines. Write them in the space below. Make sure you write in the third person. Don't use 'I' or 'me'. You are telling the story as it happens to Callie.

1. ______________________________

____

____

2. ______________________________

____

____

3. ______________________________

____

____

Still in your group, choose one of your storylines and devise a story to be spoken through. Story theatre tells a story through a number of narrators. The narrators also take on the roles of the characters.

Use the space below to plan your story theatre. Include the main ideas, each group member's role and some of the dialogue you will use. Use another piece of paper if you need to.

____

____

____

____

____

____

Right, let's write!

Name ____

Write a story about an argument between two friends.
Here are some things to think about to get you started.

- Who are the main characters?
- What is the setting?
- What is the argument about?
- How do the characters feel as the argument is going on?
- How is the argument resolved (worked out)?

Use the rest of this page to plan and draft your work before you edit and write your final version.

Introduction to The Roughtail Lizard Dreaming

Level: Year 3 Term 2

Text type: Legend from another culture

NLS objectives:

Y3T2 T1: to investigate the styles and voices of traditional story language – collect examples, e.g. story openings and endings; scene openers, e.g. 'Now when…', 'A long time ago…';

Y3T2 T9: to write a story plan for own myth, fable or traditional tale, using story theme from reading but substituting different characters or changing the setting.

The text:

Things to talk about:

What is a legend? A traditional tale, often from another culture, which has been retold over the years to pass on a meaning or explanation about nature.

Where is this legend from? The clues are in the publisher's name, the place-names in the story, and the idea of Dreamtime in Aboriginal culture.

Read the text aloud, and ask the class what they think the story means. The key is: how different races of people came to be.

The worksheets:

Readers are encouraged to make sense of the story first by making notes, and then making a map of the structure. They then act out the story, in silence; and finally, write their own 'family legend', considering the events that change in the re-telling.

The Roughtail Lizard Dreaming

A long time ago in the Dreamtime, there lived a Roughtail Lizard man who had a lot of Dreaming and songs he kept to himself. One day he was sitting by a waterhole called Ngamarlu, when some men, who were staying by the water, heard him singing.

Night after night those men got up to listen to that Roughtail man singing his songs as he sat by the fire. Every day when the men passed his camp they heard his singing. All the old people came together and they sat around, talking among themselves. They decided to send someone to meet him. "Go and ask that Roughtail man to sing us a song," they said. That person went over and asked him, "Show us how to sing one of your songs."

The Roughtail man answered, "Certainly! I'll give you my songs to learn." Then he called them all together and made them sit down and he gave to each man a song. He was putting white ochre on their chests, saying to them, "I'll give you this white ochre to put on your chests. All these songs are to be sung with ochre."

One by one he gave each man a different song. Over and over he put the white ochre on them, telling them, "This day I'm giving all these songs to the men. When I put this stuff on your chests, you may start to sing."

Then he began singing for them and as he sang he showed them dances. When he had finished he said, "I give these songs to the men to keep, each one in his own camp, a different song for each."

And so from North to South, from East to West, each has his song from the Dreamtime. Today if you go over there to Wirrumanu you can see this waterhole called Ngamarlu.

From Tjarany Roughtail by Gracie Greene and Joe Tramacchi
(Magabala Books Aboriginal Corporation)

Find the narrative

Name ______________________________

Narrative texts usually have a number of steps in their structure.
Pick out the steps in *The Roughtail Lizard Dreaming.*

Orientation ______________________________

____

____

____

Complication ______________________________

____

____

____

Sequence of events ______________________________

____

____

____

____

____

Resolution ______________________________

____

____

Coda (or final comment giving meaning) ______________________________

____

____

____

Draw a map

Name ____________________

Draw a map showing the main features of the story. Make sure you include all the events and places you mentioned in the previous activity.

Mime

Name ______________________________

Work in a group of four or five to prepare a mime about the Roughtail man. A mime is a re-telling of the story in a silent performance.

Use this space to make notes as you organise your performance. Think about ways to communicate what is happening. Actions, gestures, facial expressions and the physical organisation of your group during the performance will help.

Don't forget to rehearse!

My family's story

Name ____________________

Tell a partner a story that your family often tells. It might be a story about something that happened before you were born, when you were a baby or just last week.

Now give the story a name and answer the questions below.

The name of my family's story: ____________________

When did you first hear it? ____________________

Who told it? ____________________

Does anyone else tell it? ____________________

Do they tell it in the same way? ____________________

Why is the story important to your family? ____________________

Record it in writing

Record your story in writing. Remember to use the structure of a narrative and give your story an orientation, complication, series of events, resolution and final comment! Draft your story on rough paper first, then write your final version in the space below.

____

____

____

____

____

____

____

____

____

____

____

____

Introduction to Two fables

Level: Year 3 Term 2

Text type: Fables

NLS objectives:

Y3T2 T2: to identify typical story themes, e.g. trials and forfeits, good over evil, weak over strong, wise over foolish;

Y3T2 T6: to plan main points as a structure for story writing, considering how to capture points in a few words that can be elaborated later; discuss different methods of planning.

The texts:

Things to talk about:

What is a fable? (A universal story with a moral lesson.)

Read aloud the first fable: what is the moral lesson?

Read aloud the second fable: what is the moral lesson?

Is there a link in subject between the two fables?

Which of the two fables does the class think is more effective, and why?

The worksheets:

The first sheet helps children describe the moral in each fable in their own words. The second sheet helps them plot the structure of Aesop's fable, and then re-tell the story. The 'point of view' re-telling should be interesting, as the first person narrator will have to adopt a position of pride! And the final sheet helps children plan and write their own fable.

Two fables

The Enemies

Two men who were enemies were on a voyage in the same boat, so naturally each tried to separate himself as far as possible from the other. One man stayed in the front, or bow, of the boat, and the other remained in the back, or stern. Without warning, a great storm arose and the boat began to sink.

"Which end of the boat will sink first?" asked the man at the stern.

"The bow will go down first," replied the captain.

"That's fine," said the man. "Then I can have the satisfaction of watching my enemy drown!'

But of course his revenge was short, for his end of the boat sank soon afterwards, and he too was drowned.

Do not rejoice in another's misfortune while you are both in the same boat.
– Aesop

Three Raindrops

A raindrop was falling out of a cloud, and it said to the raindrop next to it:"I'm the biggest and best raindrop in the whole sky!"

"You are indeed a fine raindrop," said the second, "but you are not nearly so beautifully shaped as I am. And in my opinion it's shape that counts, and I am therefore the best raindrop in the whole sky."

The first raindrop replied, "Let us settle this matter once and for all." So they asked a third raindrop to decide between them.

But the third raindrop said, "What nonsense you're both talking! You may be a big raindrop, and you are certainly well shaped, but, as everybody knows, it's purity that really counts, and I am purer than either of you. I am therefore the best raindrop in the whole sky!"

Well, before either of the raindrops could reply, they all three hit the ground, and became part of a very muddy puddle.

by Terry Jones
From *Fairy Tales* (Puffin)

What's the moral?

Name ______________________________

What is a moral? Explain it in your own words.

____

____

____

____

Read the moral at the end of *The Enemies*. In your own words, write what you think it means.

____

____

____

____

Sometimes the moral is not stated at the end of a fable. It's up to the reader or listener to work it out. Write a moral for *Three Raindrops*. Use your best handwriting!

____

____

____

____

How does each story prove the moral? Talk about it with a partner, then write your opinion on the lines below.

____

____

____

____

____

____

Story structure

Name ____________________

Imagine that you are Aesop about to tell the story *The Enemies*. Complete the table and use it to help you learn and remember the story.

Main characters	
Orientation or setting	
Complication or problem	
Main events or actions	
Resolution	
Coda or moral	

Rehearse the story, and then tell it to a group of friends. How did it go? Review your storytelling.

Strengths ____________________

____

Areas to work on ____________________

____

Point of view

Name ______________________________

Point of view

Stories are usually told by a narrator. The narrator in both these fables is an outsider not involved in the action. This is called third person. Choose one of the fables and rewrite it in first person – that's from the point of view of someone involved in the action of the story.

Write a fable

Name ______________________________

Now it's your turn to write a fable. Use the table to plan your fable before drafting, editing and writing your final version on separate paper.

My Fable Plan	
The moral my fable will prove	
My fable characters	
The setting of my fable	
The problem in my fable	
The series of events in my fable	
The resolution of my fable	

Introduction to The Boy Who Bounced

Level: Year 4 Term 2

Text type: Fantasy adventure

NLS objectives:

Y4T2 T1: to understand how writers create imaginary worlds, particularly where this is original or unfamiliar, such as a science fiction setting and to show how the writer has evoked it through detail;

Y4T2 T10: to develop use of settings in own writing, making use of work on adjectives and figurative language to describe settings effectively.

The text:

Read the story aloud to the class. Things to talk about:

Is it a true story? How can you tell?

What do you think will happen next?

What do you think will be the purpose of the story?

The worksheets:

There are only two characters in this story (apart from the parents); but what do we learn about these two? Group discussion of the fantasy genre on the second sheet should be beneficial. Story planning is a crucial stage, and plenty of support is given before the writing stage. And finally, the map should help children plot the travels of their character.

The Boy Who Bounced

Once there was a little boy who had a very bad habit indeed. He used to bounce like a ball. Wherever he went his mother would say: "Walk like a little gentleman." But he wouldn't. He bounced instead. His father said: "No-one in our family has ever bounced before. I wish you would do something else. You could run a bit, or even hop, or you could skip."

The little boy took no notice at all. This was a mistake because one day he bounced on a magician who was snoozing in the sun. The magician was very cross.

"It is really too much," he cried. "I came out for a quiet day in the country and what happens? First I'm chased by a bull (I had to turn it into a canary bird to get away). Then I'm chased by the farmer who owned the bull (I had to change a foxglove into a lot of money to pay him). It has left me very tired. I lie down to have a snooze and a nasty little boy comes and bounces on me. Pah! Say you're sorry, little boy, and walk off quietly."

The rude little boy took no notice of the magician. He started to bounce away. The magician became very angry indeed.

"If you want to bounce, well, bounce you shall," he declared, and began to mutter magic words very quickly. The little boy felt suddenly strange about the fingers and toes – a sort of pins and needles feeling. (That was the magic working.) Before he could say "Mousetrap!" he had turned into a red rubber ball – a big ball, a bouncing ball. He could bounce so softly that he wouldn't break a cobweb if he bounced on it. He could bounce as high as a pine tree.

"Meet me here in a year's time," the magician said, "and I'll think about whether or not to turn you into a boy again." Then he lay down and began to snooze once more.

by Margaret Mahy.

From *The Boy Who Bounced and Other Magic Tales* (Puffin)

Character portraits

Name ______________________________

What do you think the boy and the magician looked like? Draw them in the boxes. Next to the boxes, write five things about each character which you think describe them well. The words may come from the passage, or you could think of your own.

Magician

The boy who bounced

What a fantasy!

Name ______________________________

The Boy Who Bounced is a fantasy. A fantasy is a story which is touched by magic and 'unreal' happenings. What can we learn from fantasies? Did you learn anything from this passage from *The Boy Who Bounced*? Now it's your turn to bounce! What might happen if you could bounce all over the world? Where might you go? Who might you meet? What adventures might you have?

Talk about it in a small group. Record your group's main ideas here.

What can we learn from fantasies?

____

____

____

Did you learn anything from this passage?

____

____

____

What might happen if you could bounce all over the world?

____

____

____

____

____

____

____

____

____

Write about it!

Name ______________________________

On another sheet you will find a map of the world, and lines for you to write a story based on the ideas you talked about in your group. Use the table below to help you plan your story.

Characters

Name	Description

Orientation

When and where is the story happening?

____

____

Complication or problem

____

____

Sequence of events

	Place	Event
1		
2		
3		
4		

Ending

How will the story end? Will the main character change his or her behaviour or ideas as a result of the adventures?

____

____

Bounce around the world

Name ______________________________

On rough paper, draft and edit your story. Write your final copy on the lines below and mark your journey on the map. You might need an atlas to help you find and name the places you visit.

Introduction to Jason's Walk

Level: Year 4 Term 3

Text type: Story that raises issues

NLS objectives:

Y4T3 T1: to identify social, moral or cultural issues in stories, e.g. the dilemmas faced by characters or the moral of the story, and to discuss how the characters deal with them; to locate evidence in text;

Y4T3 T8: to write critically about an issue or dilemma raised in a story, explaining the problem, alternative courses of action and evaluating the writer's solution.

The text:

Read the text aloud to the class. Things to talk about:

Why do children think Jason was failing to walk?

Why do children think Jason suddenly started to walk?

Which is the crucial sentence in the story that describes the turning-point?

Do you see any similarities with the last story? How do the parents respond in each of the stories?

What would you say is the issue dealt with in both stories?

The worksheets:

The follow-up activities start with children talking in pairs about the issue behind the story. This extends into considering the roles of each of the other members of the family. Children are then encouraged to define each of the stages of Jason's life so far. Finally, they apply their understanding of the story to retelling it in a different genre.

The section ends with helpful templates for children's own story writing.

Jason's Walk (part 1)

Jason was two-and-a-half years old. But he could not walk.

When he was six months old Jason sat up. He looked up at the world and it was a very big place. His parents were mountains. His big brother towered over him. Beanie, the big black family dog, loomed over him and licked his face.

Jason looked at the world and then he lay down again and watched it all swim above his head.

For six more months Jason lay on his back on the floor and watched the world swirl around him. His mother took him outdoors and sat him on the grass. Jason rolled over onto his back and watched the clouds whirl across the sky.

Jason's father put him on his tummy on a rug in front of the fire. Jason rolled over onto his back and looked at the firelight flickering on the ceiling.

At Jason's first birthday party Jason's brother lifted him up onto his feet to blow out the candle on his birthday cake. Jason blew at the candle but it wouldn't go out. His brother helped him blow it out. Then Jason flopped down onto the floor, rolled over onto his back and watched his family fussing over the cake.

Jason liked his worm's-eye view of the world. But his parents became anxious.

When he was one-and-a-half years old they took Jason to a doctor. The doctor held Jason's legs and measured them and prodded and poked and shook her head.

"I cannot find anything wrong," she said gravely. And she gave Jason's parents a letter of referral to another doctor.

The next doctor x-rayed Jason's legs and pulled and pushed and prodded and poked. She also shook her head.

"It's really got me puzzled," she sighed. And she gave Jason's parents letters of referral to lots of other doctors.

All the doctors looked at his legs, and measured them, and prodded and poked and wondered and sighed. And each time they put him onto his feet he simply flopped down to the floor, rolled over onto his back and looked up into their puzzled peering eyes.

Jason liked to look at their eyes staring down at him. They looked like fish eyes in a glass bowl. It made him giggle and gurgle inside.

When they got back home Jason's parents would put him on the rug in the middle of the living room and look down at him sadly and shake their heads. Jason's brother would look at him too. Beanie would stare down at him with his twinkling eyes and lick his face.

Jason's Walk (part 2)

At his second birthday party Jason's brother lifted him up to blow out the two candles on the cake. Jason didn't have any trouble blowing out the candles this year. But as soon as he had blown them out, he flopped down onto the floor and rolled over onto his back and looked up at the world.

After a while Jason's parents stopped worrying about why Jason wouldn't walk. They simply put him on the floor and let him lie on his back all day. His mother became preoccupied and seemed not to notice him as he lay on the floor watching the world swimming above him.

When Jason was two-and-a-half years old he saw his father carrying his baby basket into his bedroom. His mother came in with his baby bath. Then his brother brought in Jason's baby toys. Jason lay on his back and watched. He wondered why they were doing this.

A few days later Jason woke very early. A strange sound had aroused him. He opened his eyes and looked up. He could see the early morning patterns of light on the ceiling of his bedroom. His baby basket was making a gentle rocking movement. His baby basket was making a giggling, gurgling sound.

Jason slid out of bed onto the floor. He lay on his back for a moment. Then he stood up on both feet. He walked over to the baby basket and looked down into it. Lying on the white pillow was a soft pink face, with twinkling blue eyes. Jason looked down at the face and smiled.

Then Jason heard a movement behind him. Jason's mum and dad were kneeling beside him. He looked down at them. They were smiling too.

"Jason, this is your new baby sister," they said.

by Wendy Michaels

Let's talk about it

Name ______________________________

Jason's Walk is a realistic narrative. It tells the story of a young boy who did not walk at the age when we usually expect children to learn to walk. Talk with a partner about why you think Jason did not walk. Write your ideas in the space provided.

Change the ending of the story by writing the resolution.

The family

Name ____________________

The story is about a family. At first there are four people in this family. At the end of the story there is a fifth member of the family. Talk with a partner about your impression of the mother, father and brother in the family. Write a brief description of each of them in the space below and draw the characters as they appear to you.

mother ____________________

father ____________________

brother ____________________

Time passes

Name ______________________________

The story tells you when each of the events occurred.
Talk with a partner about the timeline for the events in the story. Write down the words or phrases that tell you about the time that has passed in the story.

____

____

____

____

____

Draw Jason as you believe he would appear at different stages in the story.
Label the drawings.

What a drama

Name ______________________________

Work in a small group to create a drama out of this story. You could create seven scenes. You will need to think about dialogue as well as action for each scene. Do your drafts on rough paper. Try out your scenes as you write them. Write the final version in the space below. Then work with your group to rehearse the play and present it to other groups in the class.

Scene 1 Jason at six months

____

____

____

____

Scene 2 Jason's first birthday party

____

____

____

____

Scene 3 Jason at the doctor's

____

____

____

____

Scene 4 Jason at home after the doctor's

Scene 5 Jason's second birthday

Scene 6 Jason at two-and-a-half

Scene 7 Jason's sister

Narrative outline

Name ______________________________

Setting	Main characters

Orientation

Complication

Series of Events

Coda/Resolution

Narrative scaffold

Name ____________________

Orientation

When? ____________________

Where? ____________________

Who? ____________________

What situation? ____________________

Why? ____________________

Complication

A problem that must be resolved occurs.

Series of events

1 ____________________

2 ____________________

3 ____________________

Resolution

The problem occurring in the complication is resolved by one of the main characters.

Re-orientation (optional)

Narrative writing interview

Name ____________________

Self-assessment e.g. What do you like writing about? Is there anything you don't like writing about or find difficult to write about? How do you rate yourself as a writer?

Range and preferences e.g. What kinds of texts do you like writing? What do you like writing about and for what type of audiences? How do you make your writing clear and interesting?

Skills e.g. How do you plan your stories? How do you edit your work? Are your ideas more important, or accurate spelling and correct sentence structure? How do you check spelling if you are unsure of a word?

Current projects e.g. What are you writing now? Which parts are you happy with and which do you think need more thought? What would you like to write?

Narrative skills checklist

Name ______________________________

Name:				
Class:	**Date/Level**	**Date/Level**	**Date/Level**	**Date/Level**
PURPOSE				
Demonstrates understanding of the purpose of narratives.				
STRUCTURE				
Writes a clear orientation.				
Creates complications based on unexpected events.				
Writes a well-developed series of events.				
Able to tie up ends in a clear resolution.				
Able to recognise different types of narratives.				
TEXT ORGANISATION				
Develops a well-sequenced plan for narrative writing.				
Writes a well-developed and clear orientation.				
Uses paragraphs correctly for new stages in the text or new developments in the complication.				
Able to write a clear sequence of events.				
Writes a resolution connected to the orientation and complication.				
LANGUAGE FEATURES				
Makes use of clear images in descriptions.				
Uses conjunctions to sequence events.				
Uses action verbs correctly.				
Uses correct tense.				
Uses dialogue correctly to build up interesting narratives.				
Uses first and third person correctly.				
Writes interesting opening sentences.				

LEVEL CODES 1 Consistently evident 2 Sometimes evident 3 Not evident

Narrative writing assessment

Name ______________________________

Task e.g. narrative, procedure, recount
Context e.g. individual, pairs, group, teacher directed

ANALYSIS

Content e.g. purpose, text organisation, awareness of audience
Skills e.g. planning, drafting, editing, redrafting, spelling, punctuation, handwriting
Language study e.g. use of adjectives, adverbs, complex sentences, link between sentences
Teaching needs e.g. attitude to task, teaching needed for further development